This 1999 Cub Scout
Annual belongs to

Name ..LYNDSEY.....................

Age ..39.....

I am a member of the ....

.................................Cub Scout Pack

My Cub Scout Promise
I promise that I will do my best
to do my duty to God and to the Queen,
to help other people and to keep
the Cub Scout Law.

£5.75
UK only

C000176338

Contents

6	Storytime	Red Six in... Murder Mystery Mayhem!
10	Find Out About	Getting On Your Bike
12	Let's Visit	Cub Scout Friends
14	Let's Play	Treasure Hunts
16	Find Out About	The Dormouse
18	Let's Explore	Back to the Future
20	Let's Play	Skills Football
22	Storytime	The Story of Icarus
24	Let's Play	Goal!
26	Storytime	The Street Smart Gang
30	Let's Explore	Volcanoes
32	Find Out About	Being Waterwise
34	Let's Make	A Waterwise Water Filter

36	Let's Explore	Town and Country
40	Storytime	Anton the Anteater in... Anton Steps Out
44	Rhymetime	Woof, Woof!
46	Food Fun	Pizza Party
48	Let's Play	Number Puzzles and Games
50	Find Out About	Adopting a Tree
52	Let's Explore	Life at the Ends of the Earth
54	Find Out About	The Cub Scout Challenge
56	Let's Explore	Maps
58	Competition	Books, Books, Books
60	News	And the Winner Is...

Safety Notice
Please note that some
activities require adult help
and supervision.

Text: Sarah Peach   Illustrations: Rob Sharpe

Getting On Your Bike

Cycling is fun, but it's very important that you and your bike are safe.

Before setting out...

always check your bike to make sure that it is safe:

- Check brakes. When the brakes are fully on, the whole of the brake block should touch the wheel rim. Brake blocks do wear down, so make sure yours are in good working order.

- Check tyres. If you can push in the sides of the tyres, they need pumping up. If you think you might have a puncture, blow the tyre up and see if it quickly goes flat again.

- Check lights. Check that batteries are working before you need them. Make sure both front and back lights are clean and shine brightly.

- Check reflector. Keep your back reflector free from dust and mud so that it is easily seen.

What to wear

Remember, cycling isn't about being in fashion, it's about being safe!

- Always wear a cycle helmet that has been tested for safety. It must fit you properly.

- Wear light or bright coloured clothing, especially if you are cycling in bad weather or when it is getting dark, so that other road users can see you.

Always ask an adult to help you make any adjustments to your bicycle.

Text Karen Hankey   Illustrations: Brian Folkard

Every so often

- Give your bicycle a good clean. If you wash away dirt it will work better and last longer. Turn it upside down (so you don't have to lean it against anything) and wash with soapy water.

- After drying, re-oil all the moving parts on your bike to keep them working smoothly. Oil:

    chain

    brake mechanism (but NOT the brake blocks. If any oil spills on them, clean it off quickly).

    jockey wheel

    front and rear mechanism (moving parts)

- Check the height of your bicycle. You are growing quickly, and may need to adjust it every few months. When the seat is at the right height you should be able to stand astride your bike with your feet touching the ground on both sides. You should be able to reach your handlebars comfortably when looking straight ahead.

Remember...

- Pavements are for people, not cyclists. If you don't feel safe riding on the road, walk with your bike to a safe place, like a park.

- If roads have cycle lanes, use them.

- Always keep both hands on the handlebars, unless you are signalling. Keep both feet on the pedals.

- Never ride more than two abreast. Ride in single file in traffic and on narrow roads.

- Never carry anyone else on your bike.

- Learn about cycling safely on a course. Make sure you always follow the rules.

On the road

What do these road signs mean? The answers are on page 61.

1

2

3

4

Cub Scout Friends

Meet some Cub Scouts from Hertfordshire. They are here to tell you why they love Cubs so much.

"We could form a band with all the musicians in our Pack!"

"I wonder if Mum and Dad will let us practise at home?"

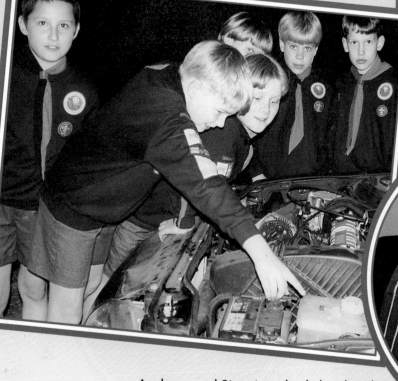

Andrew and Stuart cooked shepherd's pie for their Cook's Badge.

Text: Karen Hankey   Photographs: David Garton

Joseph has green fingers, and he's got his Gardener Badge to prove it.

"We went on a night hike. It was dark ... and a bit scary!"

What a sporty lot!

"We won't get lost!"

"I collected stamps for my Collector Badge. Got any swaps?"

The arm isn't really injured! William and Joseph are just practising first aid.

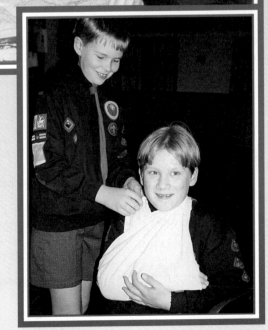

"That's why we like our Pack! Why do you like yours?"

Treasure Hunts

Treasure hunts are fun to set up, and even more fun to take part in.

Have you ever been on a treasure hunt? You might have been on one at camp, or as part of your Navigator's Badge. Why not organise one for your friends and family? You could do it in your home or garden, at your Cub meeting place, or at camp.

Treasure

- The 'treasure' can be fun-size bars, chocolates, chocolate coins, or you could write out little certificates.

Treasure hunt

You need a set of clues.
- Before you play, write 10 clues which lead to hiding places in the hunt area. You could write them in rhyme, like these:

Safety first

✘ Players need to know where the boundaries (limits) of the game are. Do not include dangerous areas like railways.
✘ Remember, you must never go anywhere on your own. Do not talk to strangers.

Off you go and take a look,
Downstairs where we keep the books
(a bookshelf).

Go to a place that's not for fishes,
It's often wet and full of dishes
(the kitchen sink).

- Hide the clues in the order the hunters have to find them. If the first clue leads to a shed, the second could lead to the garden gate, the third to the cutlery drawer, and so on.
- Say where the treasure is in the last clue. It could be some sweets hidden in a bag.
- Why not bury the bag? Make sure you get permission from the garden or sandpit-owner.
- You could draw a map as the last clue, like the one on the left.
- Make the map look old. Use a wet, used teabag and 'paint' it over the paper to stain it pale brown.

Treasure Map

HOUSE

BACKDOOR

Tree

Stand on the back door step with your back towards the house

Walk ten paces towards the tree

Turn right at the tree and walk 14 paces

·X· marks the spot – so start digging!

Illustration: Phil Garner

Text: Dave Wood

14

Number hunt

You need some card, drawing pins or sticky tabs and a pen and paper for each player.

• Cut out 26 pieces of card. Write a different letter of the alphabet on each one, from a to z. Write a number, 1, 2 or 3, on each card.

• Pin the cards around the hunt area where they can be seen. If they are indoors, use sticky tabs.

• Tell the players to find all 26 cards and to write down the number on each one on their paper.

• When they find all 26 cards, tell them to add up the numbers. If they are correct, they win the treasure!

Hunt the cards

You need card, pens and paper.

• Choose a hiding place for the treasure. Write the name of the place on pieces of card. Write one letter on each piece. For example, write 11 cards for **kitchen oven**.

• Pin or stick each card in the playing area.

• Players have to find each card and write down the letters, then rearrange them to spell out the hiding place.

• Put some treasure in the hiding place for them to find.

The Dormouse

Tiny, furry, shy and increasingly rare – let's find out more about the dormouse.

Photograph: Natural Image

Text: Brenda Apsley and Mike Brennan

If you have read **Alice in Wonderland**, you'll know about the Dormouse at the Mad Hatter's tea party. But there's more to dormice than silly poetry and falling asleep in teapots...

• The Common Dormouse is native to Britain, which means it has always lived here. Some people call it the Hazel Dormouse.

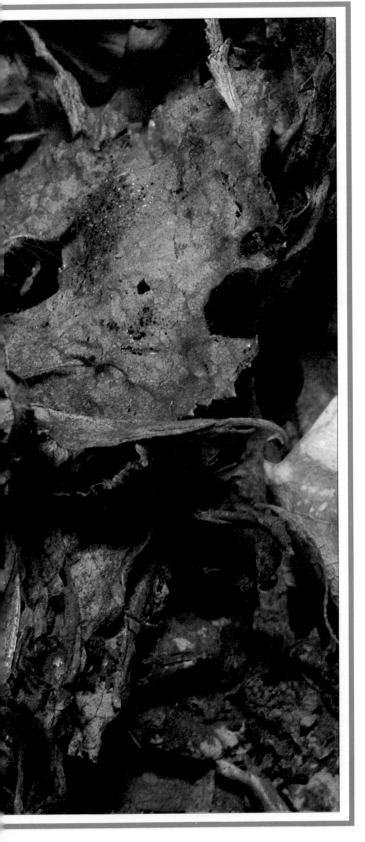

• The dormouse looks a bit like a small squirrel. It has sandy-brown fur, big eyes, round ears, short legs and a long, bushy tail. Its head and body measure about 7cm, and its tail is 7cm long.

• The dormouse lives in woods and forests. It is a climbing animal that lives mainly in trees and bushes, where it finds the things it likes to eat – nuts, bark, shoots, buds, fruits, seeds and insects.

• The dormouse builds a summer nest of bark, grass, moss and leaves. Favourite safe places are in trees or deep inside a tangle of blackberry branches. Sometimes it uses nest boxes that have been put up for birds! A shy animal, it rests during the day and comes out at night.

• The dormouse is the only British mammal that hibernates (sleeps) right through the winter. Its name means 'sleep mouse'! Autumn is a busy time for the dormouse. It eats lots and lots of food, which it stores as fat in its body, and builds an extra-warm nest on the ground, in tree roots or thick undergrowth. Then it goes to sleep – from October until April!

• The dormouse curls up into a tight ball so that it stays warm. It wraps its tail around its face like a warm, furry blanket.

• During its long winter sleep the dormouse slows down. Its heart beats just once every minute and it breathes very slowly. Its body temperature drops and it does not use its sense of sight and hearing. This is so that it can live through the cold winter using as little energy as possible. Remember, it does not eat at all!

• When it wakes up, the dormouse weighs about half what it did when it went to sleep. How do you think it feels? Yes, hungry!

• Sadly, the Common Dormouse is now an endangered species, which means that there are very few of them left.

Back to the Future

Let's find out about an old style of transport that's going to be seen on the streets of the future.

What do Manchester, Sheffield, and soon Croydon all have in common with other European cities? The answer is trams. Not the old-fashioned ones that you can still see in some seaside towns, but modern ones that are environmentally friendly. They are part of the light, rapid transport systems of the future.

Beginnings

The earliest passenger trams ran in New York in 1832. Trams were first seen in England at Birkenhead in 1861, where horses pulled carriages on wheels along metal tracks. Horses weren't the only power used: there was a steam railway in Glasgow in 1877 and one in Edinburgh in 1888 where trams were pulled along by a wire cable system.

The discovery and use of electricity sparked a boom in trams. The first electric tramway opened in Blackpool in 1885 using its famous 'balloon'

Manchester Metrolink

Text: Stephen Nixey Illustrations: Croydon Tramlink, Manchester Metrolink and London Transport Museum

double-decker trams. You can still ride on them today.

From the 1900s onwards lots of towns and cities had their own tram systems. Some had a contact 'plough' under the tram that collected power from a live rail buried in the road. This is how more than 3,000 London trams worked. Others ran below overhead copper wires which connected electricity to the trams through poles sticking up out of the roof. A system which was tried out in Torquay had 'skates' on the bottom of the tram that passed over live metal studs in the road.

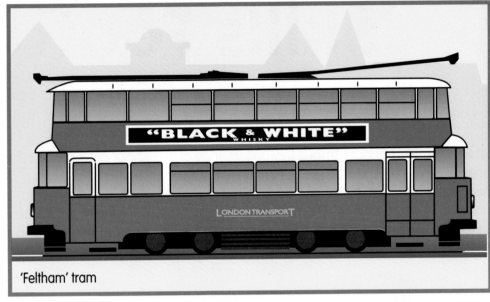
'Feltham' tram

Trams

Trams were assembled in three parts: a 'car' body, a steel underframe and a 'truck' or wheels. There were two members of staff. A driver called a 'motorman' stood up to operate the tram and had to change ends, depending on which direction the tram was travelling in. A conductor sold tickets and also had the job of throwing sand on to the tracks to help braking.

The most famous type of tram was the UCC 'Feltham', introduced in London in 1931. It was made of lightweight metal instead of wood, and seated 64 people on upper and lower decks. It had heaters, comfortable seats and enclosed cabs for the driver.

The use of trams declined due to competition from diesel-driven buses, which were cheaper to run. They disappeared from our towns and cities by the 1960s. The last London tram ran in in 1952.

The future

In 1987 the Docklands Light Railway was opened in London, the first new light rapid transport system in Britain. But it was the Manchester Metrolink system, opened in 1992, that really brought trams back to city streets.

Croydon's Tramlink is due to open by the year

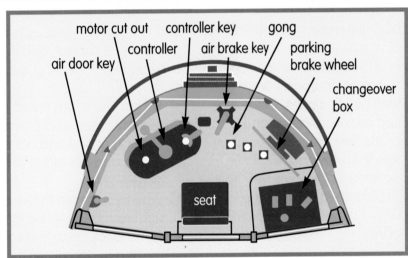
Layout of a 'Feltham' driving cab (not to scale)

2000. The 23 trams that will run on the 28-kilometre route will each carry 200 people at a speed of 80 kilometres per hour.

Trams are an old idea brought up to date by modern technology. They may turn out to be the ideal passenger transport of the future.

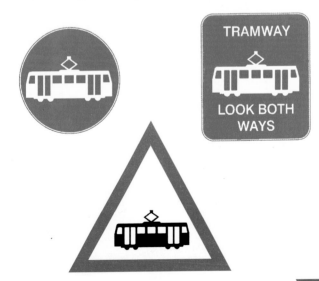

Skills Football

Have fun, get active ... and improve your football skills!

When you read about famous footballers they are often described by words like 'gifted' and 'genius'. But most footballers' skills are the result of ... hours and hours and HOURS of practice!

Playing football is good practice. But how many times in a typical game do you get the chance to shoot at goal? Or cross the ball into the box, setting up a team mate? Gaining skills outside matches is essential for every player.

Try these skills football exercises, then move on, and think up some training exercises of your own.

Equipment

The first thing is ... a football! For some activities you will also need 'obstacles', which can double as goalposts or targets. Small plastic cones, of the type used by rollerbladers and cyclists, are ideal. You can buy them from toy shops. Plastic buckets work just as well! You will also need string, rope, garden canes or a broom handle.

Slalom

This is excellent for practising general ball control, and is essential for improving dribbling skills.

- ⚽ Set up 6 or more cones in a straight line about 2m apart.
- ⚽ Starting at one end, take the ball in and out of the cones, slalom-style.
- ⚽ When you reach the end, go right round the last cone and come back down the line, moving in and out of the cones again.

⚽ Begin by using both feet to control the ball, then use one foot only. Start with your strongest foot, then use your weaker one. Using your weaker foot will be difficult, but it is worth practising. A really good footballer is able to use both feet equally well.

Target practice 1

⚽ Set up a goal by placing 2 cones 1m apart.

⚽ Stand about 3m away from the goal and ask a friend to stand 3m away on the other side.

⚽ Pass the ball to each other, aiming to make the ball go between the posts.

⚽ As you get better, start moving the posts closer together. How narrow can you make the goal and still get the ball through?

⚽ Use your stronger foot first, then your weaker one.

Target practice 2

⚽ Set up 1 cone or bucket and try to hit it time after time. Increase the distance as you get better.

Football tennis

This exercise develops chipping skills and playing the ball accurately on the volley and half-volley.

⚽ Set up some cones to make a 'tennis net' about 2m wide. Fix string to the top of the cones, or use bucket, canes or a broom handle to make a net.

⚽ Stand on one side of the net and ask a friend to stand on the other side. Kick or head the ball over the net to each other. Play this game as a one-touch exercise.

⚽ Work together as a pair, not against each other. Make your passes over the net as accurate as possible.

⚽ Play again and again, aiming to increase the number of successful passes each time.

With all aspects of training, fun and hard work should go together. If the activity is too easy, your skills will not improve and develop. If it is too hard, you will get bored and give up.

The right balance of fun and work is what you should aim for. Practise hard, but keep it fun. Who knows, one day it may be **you** who is described as 'gifted'!

The Story of
ICARUS

This is a very old story from Greece. It is a myth, a story with a meaning. Myths tell the stories of men, and the very powerful gods they believed in.

Daedalus (say it deed-a-lus) was a clever man who worked for the King of Athens.

Talos, his nephew, worked with him. He was clever, too.

"Too clever!" said Daedalus, who was jealous of him. He pushed Talos off a high roof!

A goddess turned Talos into a partridge, which is a kind of bird. He flew away to safety.

But Daedalus didn't know that! He was frightened. He ran away to the island of Crete with his son, Icarus (say it ic-ar-us).

Daedalus worked for Minos, the king. He made the Labyrinth, a big maze of passages where a monster called the Minotaur lived.

King Minos didn't want anyone to find the way in and out of the Labyrinth. He was afraid that Daedalus would tell someone, so he sent him away to an island.

Daedalus made a plan to escape. "I'll make wings using feathers and wax and string," he told Icarus. "Then we can fly away, like birds."

Daedalus fixed wings to his son's arms. "Flap them like a bird," he told him. "But be careful, my son! Don't fly too close to the sea, or your wings will get wet and be too heavy to lift."

"OK, Father," said Icarus.

"And don't fly too close to the sun," said Daedalus. "If you do, the heat will melt the wax and your wings will fall to bits."

"I'll be careful," said Icarus.

Daedalus and Icarus flapped their wings. They rose up into the air and flew away.

Icarus thought flying was the best thing he had ever done. "Look at me!" he said. "I'm flying! Wheeee!"

At first Icarus flew beside his father. But then he decided to have some fun. He zoomed high into the sky ... then swept down again. He swooped and swerved and looped and turned.

"Be careful, Icarus!" said Daedalus.

Text: Brenda Apsley   Illustration: Jon Davis

But Icarus wasn't listening...

Icarus flew higher and higher and higher. He flew closer and closer and closer to the sun.

The wax on his wings started to melt. The feathers fell off his wings.

Icarus couldn't fly without his wings, and he fell down into the sea.

Daedalus found a few feathers floating on the sea. But his son was gone.

Daedalus was very sad. He landed on an island and took off his wings. He knew that the gods had punished him by taking his son away. They did not like what he had done to Talos.

As Daedalus cried for his lost son a bird landed beside him. It was the partridge that Talos had been turned into.

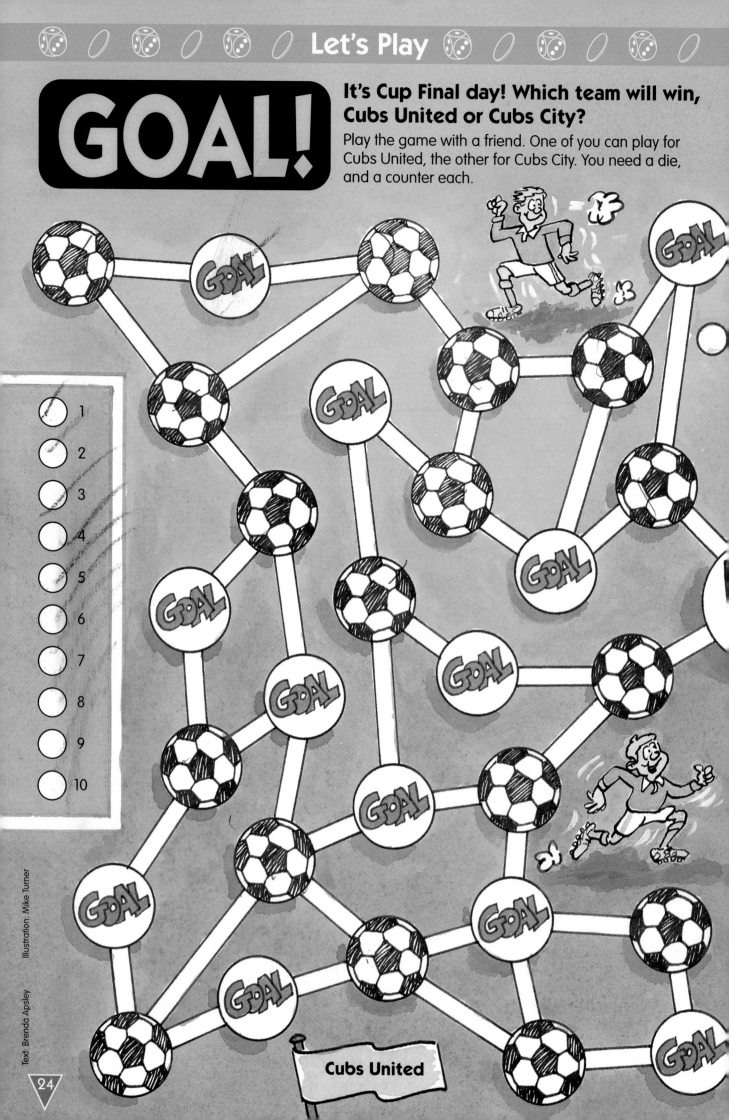

Start from the centre circle, where it says KICK OFF. Take turns to throw the die.
If you throw 1, you can make 1 move to a football.
If you throw 2, you can make 2 moves, and so on.

Move around from football to football. You score a goal when you land on a football with GOAL on it. You must use up all your score each turn, so be careful how you move from ball to ball. Like a good footballer, think ahead! You can land on the same football more than once.

When you score a goal, tick one of the balls in the OTHER team's net. The first to score 10 goals wins the Cup Final!

Cubs City

The Street Smart Gang

Text: Sara Peach   Illustrations: Jon Davis

games were not allowed in the park, and the people who lived in their street got very fed up of them dashing up and down the middle of the road on rollerblades, even though they did live in a cul-de-sac!

Simon, Rob and their friends were mad about street hockey and rollerblading, but the big problem was that they had nowhere to play. They really wanted to form a team and join a street hockey league, but they didn't think there was much chance of that when they didn't even have a pitch to play games on.

The only place they could practise was at the very top of their street, where it opened out into a wide area where cars could park. There was only one house at the top, with a large yard at the side of it. They often played up there, but just lately they had had to make a quick exit when they saw the owner of the house, Mr Daniels, watching them from a window. Sooner or later he was bound to come out and tell them off, just like all the other neighbours. Or so they thought...

It was a lovely summer's day, but Simon and Rob were fed up. As usual, there was nowhere where they could practise playing their favourite sport, street hockey. The main roads were too busy, ball

The boys were sitting in a row on the wall in front of Simon's house. They felt fed up, and were wondering what to do next when a huge concrete mixer rumbled up the street and parked in front of Mr Daniels' house. Then workmen arrived in a van, and started to concrete over the old paving stones in the yard. By the end of the day, the yard was smooth and flat.

Later, Simon and Rob were having tea when there was a knock at the door. To their horror, they heard their mum say, "Oh, hello, Mr Daniels."

"Oh, no," said Simon. "He must have come to complain about us playing hockey in front of his house. Mum'll go mad!"

"And we won't have anywhere at all to skate," said Rob.

But when Mum came back into the kitchen, she was smiling! "You're not going to believe this, boys," she said. "Mr Daniels wouldn't come in because I think he's a bit shy, but he has just told me about something very kind that he's done for you." She held out a large envelope. "He asked me to give you this."

Inside the envelope were some newspaper

cuttings and a note. The cuttings were about kids in a nearby town who had collected names, asking for the council to provide a street hockey pitch. Simon read out the note:

> Dear boys,
> I have seen how much you enjoy playing hockey, and I think you deserve a safe place to play. I have had the yard at the side of my house concreted, and I hope it will make a good practice pitch for you and your friends. Please use it any time.
>
> Tom Daniels
>
> PS: Why not collect names and ask the council for a proper pitch?

That night Simon and Rob decided on an action plan.

Next day, the first thing they did was to round up their friends and go to thank Mr Daniels.

"Thanks for your help, and your brilliant idea," said Rob.

"I'm glad to help," said Mr Daniels.

The next thing the boys did was to form a team, the Street Smart Gang. Then they collected lots of names of people who supported the idea of a street hockey pitch, and Mr Daniels sent the petition to the council.

Mr Daniels became a good friend, and acted as the team coach. He had been a PE teacher at a local college, so he knew all about hockey rules and tactics.

One day the boys were practising when Mr Daniels rushed into the yard with a letter. "It's from the council!" he said. "They're going to convert two disused tennis courts in the park into a hockey pitch!"

"Hurray!" said the boys. "Brilliant!"

The pitch was soon ready, and the Street Smart Gang were asked to play in the first game. They played against the team whose story had given Mr Daniels the idea for a petition. You can guess which team won, can't you? As Mr Daniels said, "That Street Smart Gang, they're in a league of their own!"

Volcanoes

Let's look inside a volcano to find out about these amazing natural wonders.

A volcano is an opening in the Earth's crust. A volcanic eruption is a spectacular but frightening sight. Red-hot lava bursts out from inside the Earth with a deafening roar. Mountains of fire shoot hundreds of metres into the air. Lava pours down the side of the volcano in fiery rivers that burn, bury and flatten anything in their path.

1. Volcanic soil

is very rich in chemicals. It is good, fertile soil for farmland and growing crops.

2. Layers of lava and ash

collected from previous eruptions.

3. Magma chamber

Magma is molten (liquid) rock. Pressure in the chamber causes gases to build up, forcing the magma up the central pipe.

Text: Alison Davis   Illustration: Jack Pelling

4. Poisonous gases, dust and steam

cause huge changes in the weather. Carbon dioxide raises temperatures, sulphur dioxide contributes to acid rain, and dust and ash block out the sun's rays. Steam condenses into water which may fall as rain, mixing with ash to make thick mud.

5. Central vent eruption

The more a volcano erupts, the wider the central vent becomes. Eventually it forms a crater or deep hollow.

6. Side vent eruption

Lava can flow at speeds of up to 180 metres per second.

7. Lava flow

As the lava flows it cools and hardens to form solid rock.

Geothermal energy

Scientists have found ways of using the heat inside the Earth's volcanic areas. Many houses in Iceland are heated by hot water pumped from underground. Power stations in New Zealand, Italy, America, Japan, Mexico and Chile use steam from inside the Earth to generate (make) electricity.

Being Waterwise

Water is everywhere: in the seas, in rivers and lakes, as well as in plants, and animals like you! Let's find out more about it.

Water Facts

◊ Without water there would be no life on the Earth. The whole planet would be like a dry desert.

◊ More than 70 per cent of the Earth's surface is covered by rivers and seas of water. Another 10 per cent of land is covered in ice, which is frozen water.

◊ All living things, including plants and animals, need water to live.

Waterwise

◊ Humans cannot live for more than a few days without water.

◊ About 70 per cent of your body is water. You lose water by sweating, breathing and urinating, so you must drink more to replace it.

◊ Although there is so much water on the Earth, only about 1 per cent can be used to drink.

◊ For millions of people, water is not the clean, clear liquid that comes out of our taps, but dangerous, dirty liquid that tastes bad and carries diseases.

◊ For many people in many countries, getting enough safe water is a problem they face every day. In hot parts of the world very little water falls as rain. Water is hard to find, and cannot be wasted. Often people have to walk many kilometres every day to find water, and carry it back to their homes.

◊ In many countries there is enough water, but it is made unsafe to drink by waste from cities and factories that pollutes it.

Wallaby illustrations by Ellis Nadler

Illustrations: Wendy Hesse

Text: Peter Barker

Be Waterwise: Save Water

We usually have enough water, but we should not waste it. Here are some ways in which you can help save water.

Remind your parents that when they boil water in a kettle they should use only as much as they need. Don't fill the kettle every time.

Do the washing up in a bowl, not under running water.

Keep a look-out for dripping taps and leaks. Get them repaired as soon as possible.

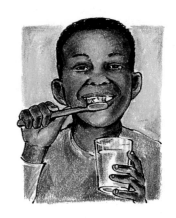

Take a shower instead of a bath – it uses MUCH less water.

Use a beaker of water when you brush your teeth – don't leave the tap running.

Put a plastic bottle of water in the toilet cistern, so that you save water every time you flush the toilet.

Can you think of any more ways of saving water?

A Waterwise Water Filter

waterwise

In places where there is not enough safe water to drink, people have to make it clean before they can use it.

People learn how to make and use special filters that turn dirty, unsafe water into clean water that is safe to drink. The most common kind of water filter uses sand to help remove dirt from water. The water then has to be boiled before it is safe to drink. These simple filters help millions of people every day. Here's how you can make one.

You will need

- large plastic fizzy drink bottle
- scissors
- stones
- small pebbles
- sand (from riverbeds or beaches)
- charcoal
- medium-size flat stone
- small piece of cloth
- elastic band
- dirty water

Illustrations: Wendy Hesse

Text: Peter Barker

1 Wash the stones, pebbles and sand.

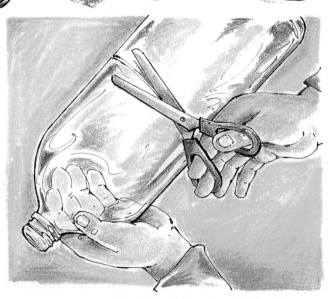

2 Cut off the top third of the plastic bottle. Get adult help for this.

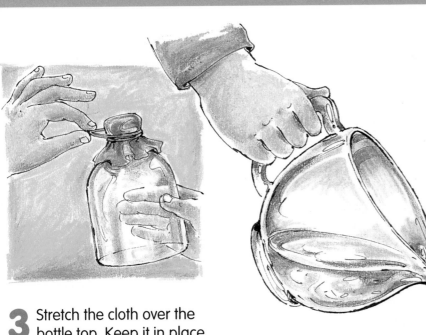

!

Even if the water you have filtered looks clean, DO NOT DRINK IT! It is NOT safe. Even though it may look clean, drinking it will make you ill, so don't try it.

3 Stretch the cloth over the bottle top. Keep it in place with an elastic band.

4 Put this upside down into the bottle base, like a funnel.

5 Put layers of stones, pebbles, sand, then charcoal into the funnel. Put the flat stone on top.

6 Pour some dirty water over the flat stone. It will travel through the charcoal, sand, pebbles and stones, which will remove many impurities. The water that collects in the bottle base will be much cleaner than the dirty water you poured in. Boiling will make it even cleaner and safer.

35

Town and Country

Dayne is from the country, John is from the town, but they both had a lot of fun at Cub camp.

"Look!" shouted Dayne to his mum. "A letter from Akela. We're having a Cub camp!" Dayne lives in a small village in the countryside and had never been to camp before, so he was really excited.

"Brilliant!" said John to his mum at their home in a busy suburb outside London. "We're having a Cub camp!"

What the two boys and their friends in two very different Cub Scout Packs didn't know was they they would all be meeting up for a weekend camp with a difference. Dayne's Akela used to run the London Pack before moving to the country, and he and the new Leader had decided to run a joint camp. The two Packs exchanged letters and photographs before the camp, so that they would get to know a bit about each other.

"The London Cubs will be rough, like on 'Eastenders'," said one of the country Cubs.

"The country kids won't know anything about anything!" said one of the London Cubs.

They were both very wrong!

James wonders where the ridge pole goes.

Text and photographs: Dave Wood

Day 1

When the Cubs arrived they were divided into Sixes, with town and country boys in each Six. There were a few groans because some of them weren't sure about being with boys they didn't know.

The tents were put up, kit laid down for the night – then it was time to explore the site!

As it got dark Cubs from each Pack paired up to play a wide game, hunting Leaders hiding in the woods. Then they went on a 'midnight hike' (though it was only 10.30!). Some Sixes decided to track other Sixes. The town Cubs told the village Cubs how to follow without being seen, as they had learned to do this recently.

The town Cubs liked looking at the black sky that shone with stars. "We've got so many street lights in London that the night sky looks all orangey!" said Francois. The country Cubs showed the town Cubs the different groups of stars. Soon it was time for bed – but not for sleep. There was too much for the new friends to talk about!

James and Richard wait for their new friends to bash in a few tent pegs.

First inspection. Do you think Andrew lost a point for losing his scarf?

The two Packs (wearing uniform above waist) see if they do a Grand Howl the same way.

37

A game of rounders before breakfast.

James plots his route for his Explorer Badge hike.

Day 2

Next morning there was a game of rounders before breakfast. After washing up and inspection, the Cubs split up into mixed groups for a morning of Explorer Badge activities like hiking, building shelters, making first aid kits – and generally having a good time.

Because there were lots of Cubs and lots of Leaders, there were lots of names to remember, so everyone wore sticky name labels. To keep it simple (or was it the Leaders having a bit of fun?) in the Aardvark Six all the boys were called James!

In the afternoon there was a grand challenge. The Cubs got a passport stamped each time they completed one of the twelve activities on it. They did interviews with other Cubs, made things, had a scavenger hunt, cracked codes, followed a blindfold trail, and lots more...

After games and supper some Guides who were camping nearby joined the Cubs for a camp fire. After songs and little plays called 'sketches' there was hot chocolate and cake for everyone.

Yum! Sausages, onion and tomato barbecued on a skewer.

And for pudding – toasted marshmallows and toffee apples.

Day 3

On Sunday the Cubs tried Scouting skills like fire lighting, tracking, cooking over fires, orienteering, compass work and tree climbing. Then it was time to pack up the tents and head for home.

"I thought the town Cubs would be rough," said Peter. "But Joe's a good friend now. He's in a drama group and I'm going to see his next show."

"I thought the country Cubs would only be interested in horses and sheep and stuff like that," said Ian. "But Tom supports Manchester United and likes rollerblading, just like me!"

Some of the town and country Cubs keep in touch and have met up for birthday parties and football matches. Some watched 'Ice Warriors' being filmed.

When the Leaders asked what sort of camp they wanted this year, both Packs said, "We want to go with the other lot again!"

The London Cubs were nothing like the kids on 'Eastenders', and the country Cubs were nothing like those on 'Emmerdale'! Meeting up at camp taught them that you shouldn't judge people before you get to know them. That way you'll have a nice surprise when you find out that they're really just like you!

Akela A starts a tracking exercise.

"I hope Mum doesn't see this!" Tom and Simon do the washing up.

Kaa B and King Louie show the Cubs how to use a compass.

Anton the Anteater in ...
Anton Steps Out

Anton is a very unusual anteater. He wears glasses, a baseball cap, a bow-tie and trainers with flashing lights, but that's not what makes him really unusual...

Anton lives with lots of other anteaters in the middle of the jungle in South America. His best friend isn't another anteater, but a small round pebble he calls ... Pebble. His second best friend is a sort of mousey, voley creature called Horatio who Anton trod on one day. After the getting-trodden-on-by-a-large-anteater incident, he rides around in a wheelchair.

"What's for tea, Mum?" asked Anton one teatime.

"Ants," said Mum.

"But I don't like ants," said Anton. (See? I said he was unusual, didn't I?)

"It's ant stew," said Mum.

"If it's got ants in it I won't like it," said Anton.

"I could open a tin of soup," said Mum.

"Ant flavoured?" asked Anton.

"Yes," said Mum. "Or how about some strawberry surprise?"

"What's the surprise?" asked Anton.

"Er ... ants," said Mum.

Anton went to his room. He lay on his bed and looked at a poster of his favourite rock group, Stonehenge. It gave him an idea. "I'll run away to England," he said. "I might find a food that I like."

He packed his pyjamas, the longest toothbrush you have ever seen, and Pebble. Then he wrote a note:

> **Going around the world.**
> **Might be late.**
> **Love, Anton.**
> **PS: Will send a postcard.**

Anton called for Horatio, and they set off. It took them three years to walk to the coast.

"Our ship, she go to Eengerland," said a sailor. "We take you weeth us."

Anton and Horatio followed the sailor to the ship. "Anton, I don't like the way that sailor is looking at you and licking his lips," said Horatio, who knew that sailors like Roast Anteater.

On board, the sailor opened an oveny-looking door. "Thees ees your cabin," he said, turning a switch to mark 8. "Climb inside. We weeel eat later."

"Get out of there!" said Horatio as soon as he had gone. "This is an oven – and you're dinner!"

Anton and Horatio spent the rest of the trip hiding inside a big funnel. They played a game for people who can't spell, called Skrobbel.

Text: Dave Wood   Illustrations: Jo Turner

The days turned into nights, the nights turned into days and the days turned into nights.

Then... "Land!" said Anton.

They slid down a rope to the harbour and set off to find Stonehenge.

"Which way should we go?" Anton asked Pebble.

Pebble said nothing, so Anton put him back in his pocket. But he missed, and Pebble hit the back of Horatio's wheelchair. It tipped over backwards and Horatio found himself staring up at a road sign. "Look, a sign from above!" he squeaked. "Stonehenge this way!"

Before you could say "slphjhdhvenxjn-giblkegogogoch" they were standing on a hill looking down at the circle of big stones. "Whoopee!" shouted Anton, and ran down the hill.

Horatio sped along behind him, but he crashed into a big stone. "My wheel has fallen off!" he said. "We'll never get there now!"

Anton and Horatio cried and cried and cried. So did Pebble.

Just then, along came some Cub Scouts. "Look, Ella," said Timothy. "There's an anteater and a mousey, voley thing over there, and they look upset. Let's take them with us and see if we can help."

The boys and girls carried Anton and Horatio to some green huts made of cloth. There was a big fire.

"These poor animals look hungry," said Timothy.

"The small one looks like a mouse or a vole," said Oliver. "I'll give him some cheese."

"What about the other one?" said Ella. "He looks like an anteater. Shall we find some ants for him?"

Anton looked sad. Surely he hadn't come all this way to eat ants?

"You must be joking!" said Timothy. "I'm not collecting ants! I'll go and ask Akela for some baked beans instead."

Timothy came back with the beans. Anton stared at the plate, then he pushed his long pointy snout close to it, and out came his long, thin tongue. It picked up a baked bean and put it into his mouth. Anton chewed a bit ... swallowed ...and smiled the biggest, smiliest smile that an anteater has ever smiled.

"I like baked beans!" said Anton, and he didn't stop munching until he had eaten every one. He moved his snout around the plate like a vacuum cleaner until it was spotless.

"Perhaps we could adopt these two as mascots for our Pack," said Oliver. "Akela works on a farm, so they could live there. We could look after them and feed them on cheese and baked beans."

Anton liked the sound of this, even though he was so busy smiling. So did Horatio. "No more ants!" thought Anton. "Baked beans forever!"

Anton, Horatio and Pebble had a very happy life on the farm. They played with the Cub Scouts when they came to visit, wrote postcards home – and ate lots and lots and lots of baked beans.

See? I said Anton was an unusual anteater, didn't I?

Woof, Woof!

These funny poems are anonymous,
which is a long word that means
we don't know who wrote them!

I've Got a Dog

I've got a dog
   as thin as a rail,
He's got lots of fleas
   all over his tail.
Every time his tail
   goes flop,
The fleas at the bottom
   all hop to the top!

Illustrations: Mike Turner

The Shaggy Dog

There was a young boy nicknamed Baggy,
Whose dog was enormous – and shaggy.
   The front end of him
   Looked vicious and grim,
But the tail end was friendly – and waggy!

Pizza Party

Pizzas are perfect food for lazy people who order
by phone and have them posted through the letter box!
Have fun making your own.

Before you begin

- Wash your hands
- Put on an apron
- Ask an adult to help you
- Collect the things you need

Crusty bread pizza

1 Lay the crust end piece of a loaf of **bread** flat. Put a large mug or small bowl on top, upside-down. Press down really hard to cut out a circle.

2 Put some **tomato sauce** (also called ketchup, or catsup in America!) on the soft side of the bread. Spread it with the back of a teaspoon.

3 Grate some **cheese** (such as Cheddar) and sprinkle it over the tomato sauce.

4 Put the pizza under the grill for about 5 minutes until the cheese starts to bubble. Let it cool down...then eat!

If you like lots of toppings on your pizza, add:

- pieces of cooked ham or sausage
- pieces of red or green pepper
- chopped pineapple chunks

Text: Emma Wood   Illustrations: Wendy Hesse

Biscuit pizza

Try making the same sort of pizza using a large digestive biscuit (without chocolate!) as a crunchy base.

Pizza rolls

1 Cut the crusts off a slice of bread.

2 Cover the bread with tomato sauce, then some grated cheese.

3 Roll up into a sausage shape. Put a cocktail stick through each end to hold it together.

4 Put the pizza roll under the grill. Turn it as it starts to toast. Cool, then eat!

Party time

- Have a pizza party, and let your friends choose their own toppings.
- In the summer, take telephone orders and deliver to friends in your street.

Number Puzzles and Games

19 Nineteen

Choose a number between 1 and 20.
Write it out as a word.
If you choose 19, write NINETEEN.
Count how many letters in the word nineteen.
There are 8. Write 8 as a word: EIGHT.
Eight has 5 letters, so write FIVE.
Carry on as far as you can go.
What number do you get to?

Try this with other numbers.
Do you always end up with the same number?

One to Nine

Write the numbers 1 to 9. Write one number in each circle.

⑧ ③ ④ ⑤ ⑥ ① ② ⑨ ⑦

8 3 4 5 6 1 2 9 7 divided by 9 = 92729033
Now write the numbers 1 to 9 in a different order.
Divide the big number by 9.
It doesn't matter which order you choose.
The big number always divides exactly by 9!

Now for the hard bit! Divide the big number by 9.
You can use a calculator to make things easier.
9 divides into the number with nothing left over,
like this:

Text: Brenda Apsley   Illustrations: Jeannette Slater

48

Ones!

Can you write seven 1s in a row
so that they add up to 25?
Do it by adding plus signs.
Think about it!

$$1 \ 1 \ 1 \ 1 \ 1 \ 1 \ 1 \ = \ 25$$

Think of a Number

Ask a friend to think of two numbers between
1 and 9.
Tell him to double one of the numbers.
Add 4 to it.
Multiply it by 5.
Finally, tell him to add on the other number.
Ask him for the total.
IN YOUR HEAD, take 20 away from the total.
The two numbers left are the numbers your friend
thought of!

Here's how it works:

Your friend thinks of 9 and 8.
He chooses 9 and doubles it, making 18.
He adds 4 to 18, making 22.
He multiplies 22 by 5, making 110.
He adds the other number (8) making 118.
You take away 20 from 118, making 98.
9 and 8 are the numbers he first thought of!

The answers are
on page 61.

7 Makes 12

Write the numbers 1 2 3 4 5 6 and 7
in the little boxes. Write a different number
in each box.
Can you set them out so that each set
of 3 boxes adds up to 12?

**How do you
do that?**

It's easy!

49

Adopting a Tree

Why not adopt a tree and find out all about it?
Choose one in your garden or a local park.

Record

- Draw and colour pictures or take photographs of your tree in spring, summer, autumn and winter. Does your tree change in the different seasons of the year?

- Put your pictures in a tree scrap book or diary. Collect and write down information about your tree. Write down what kind of tree it is, where it is and how big it is.

Measure: how tall is your tree?

- Stand away from your tree, facing it. Hold up a pencil at arm's length in front of you, so that you can see it and the tree at the same time. Ask a friend to stand at the base of the tree.

- Line the pencil up so that its top is in line with the top of the tree. Move your thumb down the pencil until it is level with the base of the tree.

- Turn the pencil sideways, keeping your thumb level with the base of the tree. Ask your friend to walk away from the tree. Tell him to stop when he is level with the top of the pencil.

- Mark the place where your friend has stopped with a stick. Measure the distance from the tree to the stick. This distance is the height of your tree. Write it in your tree scrap book.

- Measure at the start of the year and at the end of the year. Has your tree grown?

Measure: how big is your tree?

- Put a piece of string around the tree trunk. Keep your finger on the place where the string meets.

- Lay the string straight on the ground and measure from the end to the place you marked with your finger. This is the distance around the tree. It is called the girth.

Collect

- In spring and summer, collect leaves, blossom and fruits from your tree. Stick them in your scrap book, or make them into a tree collage.

- In autumn, collect more leaves. You could make a leaf picture with them. Do you know why the leaves are a different colour in autumn?

Text: Emma Wood   Illustrations: Jeannette Slater (page 50) & Guy Parker-Rees (page 51)

Tree life

A tree can be a home and a safe place for lots of animals and birds. A tree provides food for many animals and birds, too.

Animals like **bees** and **owls** live inside trees, in holes and hollows.

Animals like **bats** and **squirrels** live on tree branches. Birds like **thrushes** build nests there.

Some **insects** live on and under the bark of trees.

Caterpillars live on tree leaves.

Animals like **rabbits** and **badgers** live under trees.

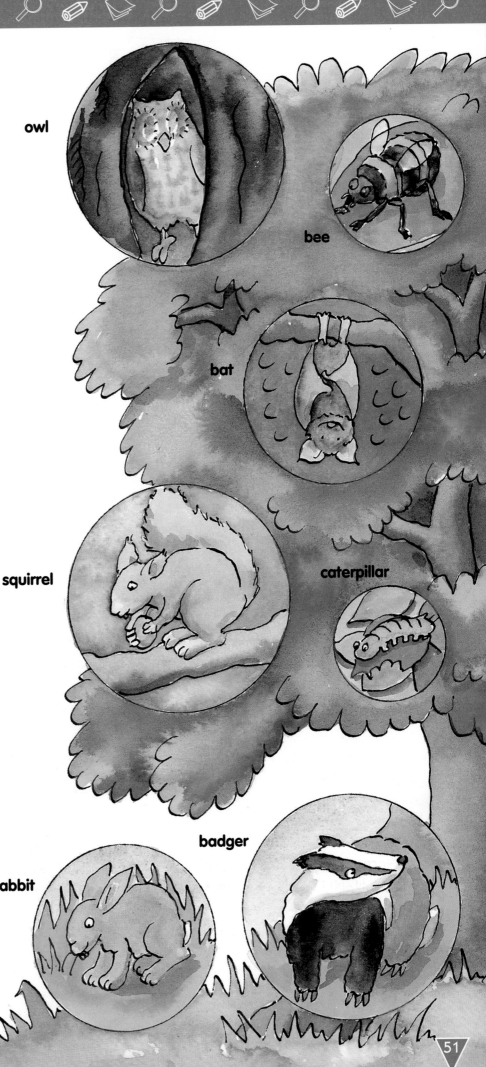

owl

bee

bat

squirrel

caterpillar

badger

rabbit

51

Life at the Ends of the Earth

Let's find out about two lands of ice and snow that are the coldest places on Earth.

The land at the top of the Earth is around the **North Pole**. It is called the **Arctic**. It is a very big ocean with land around it. A lot of the water in the ocean is frozen right through the year. Life is hard, but some animals and plants live here.

The **polar bear** has thick fur to protect it from the cold, even in icy water. The polar bear hunts mainly by smell. It catches seals, fish and birds. Cubs stay with their mother until they are about two years old. She teaches them how to hunt.

The male **walrus** can grow to 3 metres long. The female is smaller. The walrus grows two very long teeth called tusks. It uses them to dig holes in the ice.

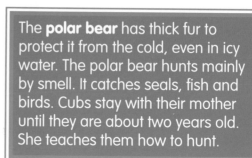

The **narwhal** belongs to the whale family. It hunts fish and squid. The narwhal has two teeth. The left tooth of the male grows into a tusk over 2 metres long.

Text: Brenda Apsley   Illustrations: David Webb

The cold land at the bottom of the Earth is around the **South Pole**. It is called the **Antarctic**. It is one enormous sheet of ice that covers a larger area than the United States of America. There is not enough plant material to feed land animals, but there is lots of life in the sea.

The **penguin** is a bird, but it cannot fly. 16 kinds of penguin live in the Antarctic. They are all expert swimmers and divers. They use their wings like flippers. When the female **emperor penguin** lays an egg, the male keeps it warm between his feet and body until it hatches.

The **leopard seal** is clumsy on land, but swims very fast in the water. It hunts penguins and other seals. The seal's oily fur and a thick layer of fat under the skin keep it warm in the coldest water. Baby seals are called pups.

The cold Antarctic seas are full of very tiny creatures that look a bit like shrimps. They are called **krill**, and are the main food of the **blue whale**, the largest animal that has ever lived. It can grow up to 30 metres long, or as long as 15 adults lined up head to toe. The blue whale can live for 80 years.

The Cub Scout Challenge

Why not complete the Cub Scout Challenge award before you move up to Scouts?

As a Cub Scout you have the chance to try many enjoyable activities, by working your way through the Progress Awards, or by gaining one or more Activity Badges. However, by the time you are nine and a half years old, you will be ready to take on some exciting new challenges which, as well as being fun, will help prepare you for your move up to Scouts.

This is where the Cub Scout Challenge comes in. It is an extra award which you can work for alongside your Progress Awards. The great thing about it is that you can undertake many of the activities with the rest of your Pack or members of your Six.

Requirements

These are the requirements of the Cub Scout Challenge. You must complete activities in each of the four sections.

Outdoor Challenge

Take part in an outdoor challenge with a Leader and other Cub Scouts which should include at least **four** of the following activities:

1 Spend at least two nights under canvas.
2 Plan and go on a hike.
3 Cook a simple meal 'backwoods' style.
4 Take part in a wide game.
5 Build a bivouac.
6 Follow a simple orienteering course.
7 Complete any other suitable activity agreed with your Leader.

Adventure Challenge

With a Leader, choose and take part in at least **two** adventurous activities.

Sharing Together

Take part in at least **three** meetings of older Cub Scouts and Leaders. Share ideas for future Pack meetings, events and outings, and help make plans for one of them.

Photographs: Chris Boardman

Text: Mike Brennan

Conservation
Help other Cub Scouts carry out a local conservation project.

Games
Organise and help run some games on a Pack night.

Over to you
Take a leading part in any other suitable activity agreed with a Leader.

Is that challenging enough for you? As you can see, the award covers a wide range of interests, and allows plenty of scope for broadening your experience within Scouting. When deciding on your Challenge activities make sure that you choose things you haven't done for one of the other awards. This will make the Cub Scout Challenge more interesting and exciting for you.

Good luck!

Full details of the Cub Scout Progress Awards and Activity Badges can be found in **The Cub Scout Handbook** (ISBN 85165 289 1), published by The Scout Association.

Helping to Lead

Take a leading part in **two** Pack activities such as:

Team captain
Act as captain for a football, swimming or cricket team, or another team of your choice.

District/County/Area event
Represent your Pack at a District, County or Area event such as a competition, quiz, Sixers' Meeting, or any other suitable event.

Camping
Be a tent leader or take on a special responsibility at camp.

Pack show
Take a leading role in a Pack show, either front or backstage.

Pack open night
Help with arrangements for a Pack open night.

Beaver Scout Colony
Visit a Colony to tell Beaver Scouts about Cub Scouts, and help run a game at a Colony meeting.

Maps

Maps tell us what the world
looks like and help us plan journeys.
But how did maps first come about?

What is a map?

- Maps are diagrams of an area. They show the surface of the Earth, which is spherical (ball-shaped), as a flat 'picture'.

- Imagine that the Earth is transparent (see-through), with a light in the centre. The features of the Earth like areas of land and sea appear as shadows on a piece of paper held close to the globe. These can then be copied to make a map. This is called map projection.

- The paper is placed flat at the North and South Poles (find out more about these areas on page 52) and rolled around the Equator like a cylinder.

- It is very expensive to make maps. Because of these high costs, most maps are made by national organisations so that everyone can buy and use them. In Britain maps are made by Ordnance Survey, which was set up in 1791. In France maps are made by Institut Geographique, and in America by the US Geological Survey.

Famous mapmakers

- The very first maps were made when travellers and guides scratched rough drawings of routes on the ground.

A typical modern map.

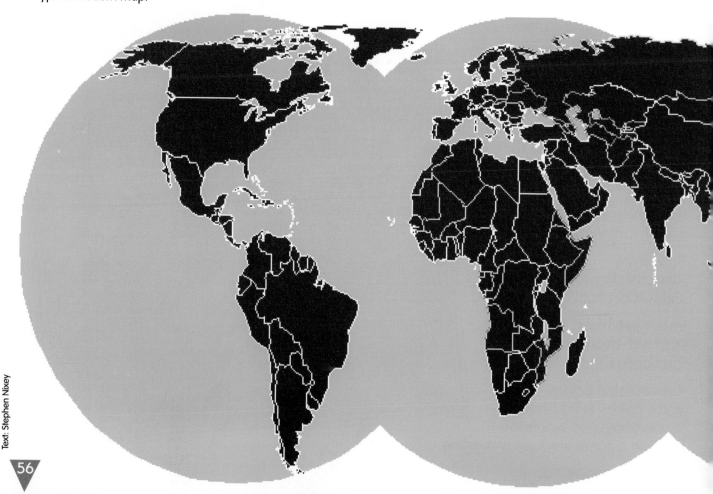

Text: Stephen Nixey

- Mapmakers are called cartographers. The first mapmakers made maps based on the journeys of early travellers. One that dates from 1030 AD was based on the journeys of Archbishop Sigeric.

- The oldest known map was made in Babylonia in about 500 BC. It was drawn on flat pieces of clay called tablets. It showed what some people thought the world looked like then – a flat area of land, not a round planet.

- A Greek astronomer and geographer called Claudius Ptolemy left detailed instructions about how to draw maps. His method is how most maps were made until quite recently.

- One Mappa Mundi (map of the world) was drawn by an English priest between 1280 and 1300. It showed the world as people thought it was then, but would not be useful for travellers today!

- An atlas is a book of maps. The first atlas of the world was produced in 1570 by Abraham Ortelius. Two two years later Gerhard Mercator and Joducus Hondius drew the globe in a flat

Roman map of Britain. Note that Scotland is facing the wrong way.

form for the first time. You can still see their Atlas of Europe in the British Library.

- The first atlas of England and Wales appeared in 1579. It was drawn by William Saxton. As well as showing features like rivers and mountains, he started using symbols for churches and castles that look like the ones we see on maps today.

Ptolemy's map of the world.

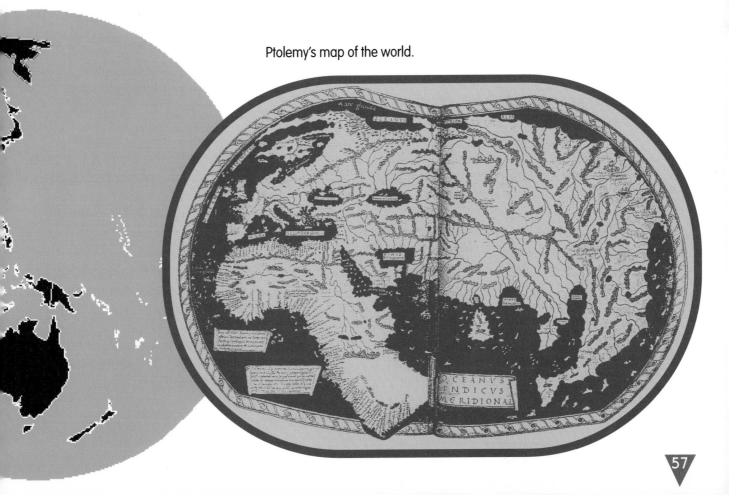

Books, Books, Books

Have fun by entering our competition. There are some great prizes for the winners.

Where would we be without books? Well, for one thing, you wouldn't be reading this Annual if books hadn't been invented! Ever since the first printed books appeared in the 1450s, books have been an essential and much-loved source of information, entertainment and pleasure. Even in this day and age, when there are such distractions as television, cinema, video games and computers, books are still enormously popular.

Here are some facts you may not know about the world of books.

 The Bible is the most widely distributed book in the world and has been translated into over 300 different languages.

 A Super Book was published in 1976 in Denver, Colorado, USA. It measured 2.74 metres by 3.07 metres, had 300 pages and weighed over 250 kilogrammes.

 The smallest book ever published was a copy of the children's story **Old King Cole**. The book measured 1 mm by 1 mm and the pages could only be turned by careful use of a needle.

 The largest library in the world is the United States Library of Congress in Washington DC, USA. The library contains over 88 million items and has 856 kilometres of shelving.

 A book borrowed from a college library in Cambridge in 1667 was returned, overdue, 288 years later.

 The greatest number of novels published by one writer is 904. They were written by Kathleen Lindsay of South Africa.

Prize contents may differ from those shown

Competition

So, you like books, do you? Well, this competition is just for you. This year the Cub Scout Annual is offering you the chance to win a bumper selection of books as the prize in the great 1999 Cub Scout Annual Book Competition.

All you have to do is answer the following three questions. Write you answers, along with your name, age and address on a postcard and send it to the address below to arrive no later than 1st February 1999. It couldn't be easier.

And don't worry, question number 3 is not a trick question. It's just for fun, so we can get an idea of the sort of books you like.

1. Who wrote **Scouting for Boys**?
2. Who wrote **The Jungle Book**?
3. What is your own favourite book or story?

The sender of the first correct entry selected at random after the closing date will win the first prize of a selection of books which will include a copy of **The Cub Scout Handbook**. Four runners-up will also each receive a copy of **The Cub Scout Handbook**.

Send your entry to:

Books, Books, Books
1999 Cub Scout Annual
The Scout Association
Baden-Powell House
Queen's Gate
London
SW7 5JS

And the Winner is...

Martin Golding
of the 2nd Royal Eltham Cub Scout Pack!

Congratulations, Martin!

Martin's badge design, shown here, was chosen as the winning entry in the 1998 Cub Scout Annual Crayola Colouring Competition. Martin's super prize is a bumper pack of Crayola goodies for himself, plus a selection of Crayola goodies to share with his Pack.

The winning design will also be made into a special pin badge for Martin and his Pack to wear.

Runners-up prizes have been awarded to:

Jason Dawes
of the 5th Portsmouth Cub Scout Pack

and

Jack Roberts
of the 2nd Bramhall Cub Scout Pack.

Congratulations to Jason and Jack, whose winning designs are shown below. Both win a selection of Crayola goodies to share with their Colonies.

There was a great response to the competition, and the standard of entries was very high indeed. A big thank you and well done to all the Cub Scouts who entered.

This year's competition is on page 58.

This is Jason Dawes' design, and...

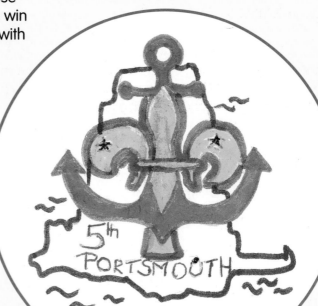

...this is Jack Roberts' design.

Answers

Getting On Your Bike page 11
1. Cycle route **2.** No cycling
3. Segregated (divided) pedal cycle and pedestrian route
4. Buses and cycles only

Number Puzzles and Games
pages 48 and 49
19 Nineteen
You always end up with 4 (four)
Ones!
$11 + 11 + 1 + 1 + 1 = 25$
7 Makes 12

```
              5
                3
                4
            2  1
          6      7
```